The Shoe Grabber

The shoe grabber
came to school.
"Shoo! Shoo!" said the teacher.
But the shoe grabber grabbed
the children's shoes.

Then the shoe grabber grabbed the teacher's shoes.

"Give us our shoes!"
they yelled.

"No!" said the shoe grabber,
and it ran away, laughing.

"Oh no!" said the teacher.
"We can't run after it.
We haven't any shoes."

"We could run with bare feet,"
said the children.

The shoe grabber
ran through the stream,
splash, splash, splash.
The teacher and the children
ran through the stream,
　　splash, splash, splash

The shoe grabber
ran through the sand,
scrunch, scrunch, scrunch.
The teacher and the children
ran through the sand,
scrunch, scrunch, scrunch.

The shoe grabber
ran through the mud,
plop, plop, plop.

The teacher and the children
ran through the mud,
plop, plop, plop.

The shoe grabber
ran through the daisies,
swish, swish, swish.

The teacher and the children
ran through the daisies,
swish, swish, swish.

They caught up
with the shoe grabber.
"Now give us our shoes!"
they yelled.

"Oh help!"
said the shoe grabber,
and it dropped the bag
and ran away.

The children and the teacher
picked up their shoes,
but they didn't put them on.

"We like bare feet,"
said the children.

"I like bare feet, too,"
said the teacher.

They ran through the daisies,
swish, swish, swish.

They ran through the mud,
plop, plop, plop.

They ran through the sand,
scrunch, scrunch, scrunch.

They ran through the stream,
splash, splash, splash,
and back to school.

And they didn't
put their shoes on...

until winter came.